Sean

GATEWAYS TO READING TREASURES
CO-BASAL LITERARY READERS

STORYLAND FAVORITES

HAROLD G. SHANE
University Professor of Education
Indiana University

and

KATHLEEN B. HESTER
Professor of Education
Eastern Michigan University

LAIDLAW BROTHERS • PUBLISHERS
A Division of Doubleday & Company, Inc.
River Forest, Illinois

Summit, New Jersey   Palo Alto, California   Dallas, Texas   Atlanta, Georgia

GATEWAYS TO READING TREASURES
CO-BASAL LITERARY READERS

A series of seven readers beginning with the Primer *Tales to Read*
followed by a book for each grade one through six.

Tales to Read

Stories to Remember

Storyland Favorites

Doorways to Adventure

Magic and Laughter

Words with Wings

Courage and Adventure

Illustrated by

MARY MILLER SALEM

COPYRIGHT©, 1966, BY LAIDLAW BROTHERS
A Division of Doubleday & Company, Inc.
PRINTED IN THE UNITED STATES OF AMERICA
4 5 6 7 8 9 0 4 3 2 1 0 9 8 7 6

STORIES and POEMS in this BOOK

4

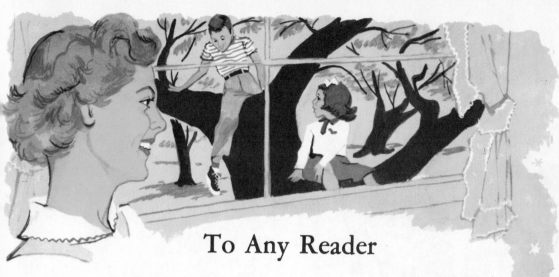

To Any Reader

As from your house your mother sees
You playing round the garden trees,
So you may see, if you will look
Through the windows of this book,
Another child, far, far away,
And in another garden, play.

Robert Louis Stevenson

The Lion and the Mouse

Have you heard the story of the Lion and the Mouse? It is a very good story.

One day a big lion was sleeping under a tree. He looked very beautiful there in the sun.

7

A little mouse began to play near the sleeping lion. Soon another mouse began to play near the lion, too.

"Look at me!" said the first mouse. "I am not afraid of this big old lion!" And he ran right over the lion's head.

The other mouse wanted to show
his friend that he was not afraid
of the sleeping lion. "Just look at
what I can do!" he said.

Then, to show that he was not
afraid, he ran right up to the
lion's head! He stopped near the
lion's mouth.

9

The lion's sleep was about over.
He heard the little mouse and he
opened one of his eyes. The mouse
was so afraid that he could not run.

Then the lion opened his other
eye. "Well!" he said, "what are
you doing here, little mouse?"

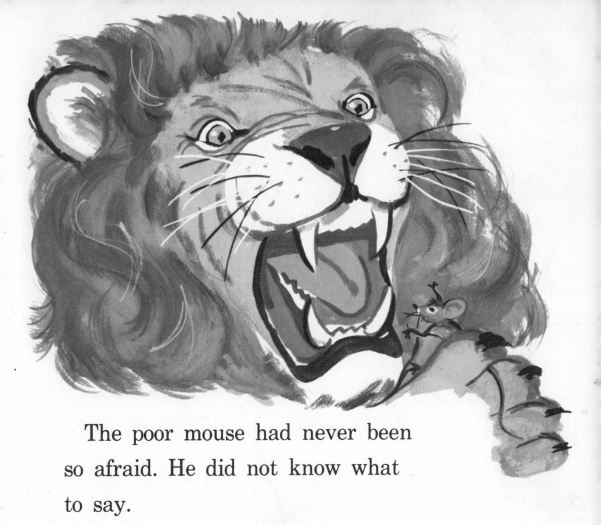

The poor mouse had never been
so afraid. He did not know what
to say.

"You bad little mouse. I think I
will eat you," said the lion.

"Oh, please do not eat me!" said
the mouse. "If you will let me go
I will help you some day."

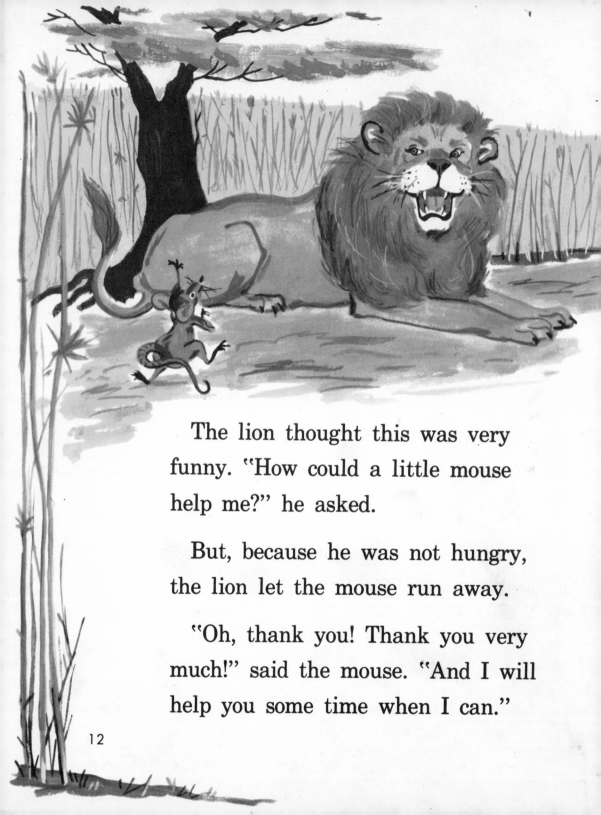

The lion thought this was very funny. "How could a little mouse help me?" he asked.

But, because he was not hungry, the lion let the mouse run away.

"Oh, thank you! Thank you very much!" said the mouse. "And I will help you some time when I can."

One day three men came to
the woods. They were going to
catch the lion.

Can you tell from the picture
how the men thought they could
catch him?

The next day the lion was out in the warm summer sun. He did not know that there was a big surprise for him when he went around the trees.

He did not know what the three men had done so that they could catch him.

Then, just like that, the lion was caught. He was caught and he could not get out.

He tried and tried to get out. And what a noise he made!

At last the poor lion saw that he could never get out.

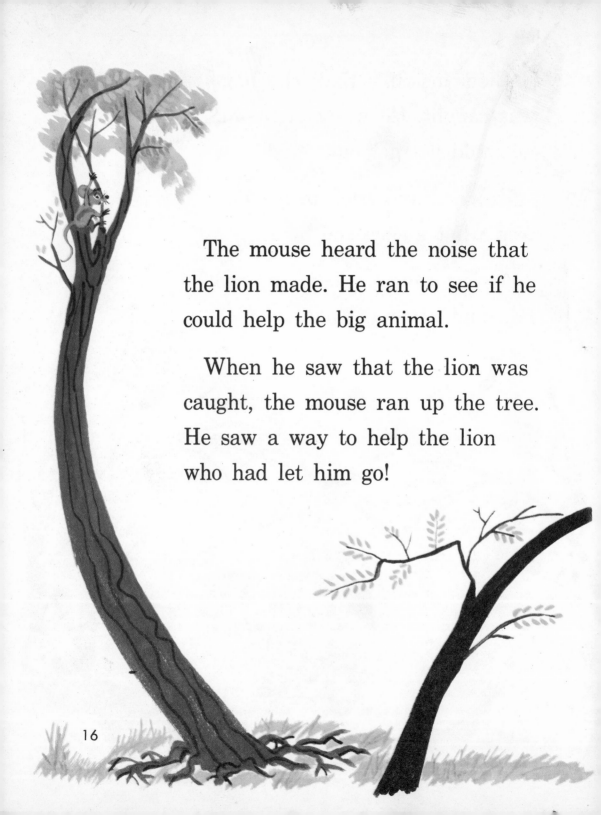

The mouse heard the noise that the lion made. He ran to see if he could help the big animal.

When he saw that the lion was caught, the mouse ran up the tree. He saw a way to help the lion who had let him go!

"Mr. Lion," he said, "you let me go a day or two ago. Now I will help you."

"No," said the lion. "Don't take time to help me. The men who caught me will be here soon. I do not want them to get you, too, little friend."

But the good mouse would not go. He began to work to get the lion out.

Then the lion heard the three men coming. "You can't help me now, little friend," he said. "Run and hide in the woods."

"No! No!" said the mouse. "I will have you out in a minute. I can do it!"

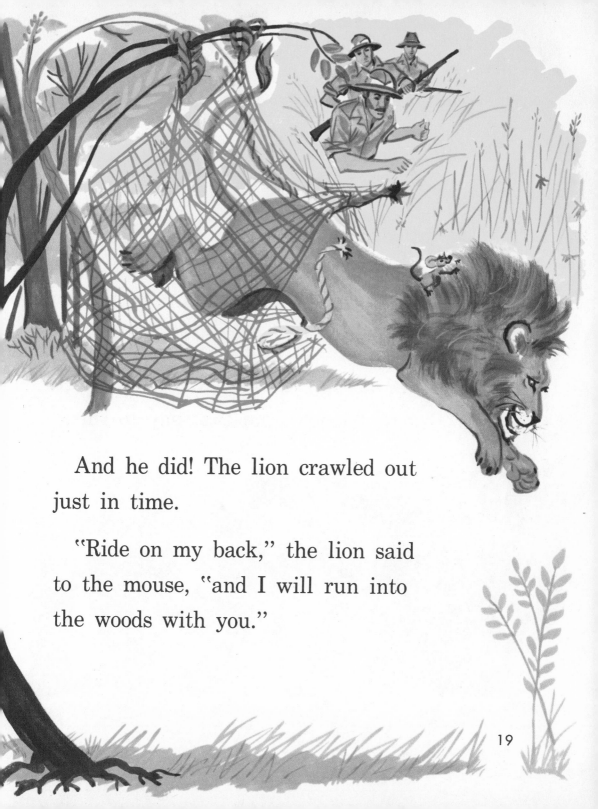

And he did! The lion crawled out
just in time.

"Ride on my back," the lion said
to the mouse, "and I will run into
the woods with you."

When the lion and the mouse
had run far from the three men,
the big animal said, "Thank you,
little mouse!"

Then he sang out, "Little friends
are good friends. Never again will
I say that a mouse is too little
to help a lion."

And the lion and the mouse were
good friends from that day to this!

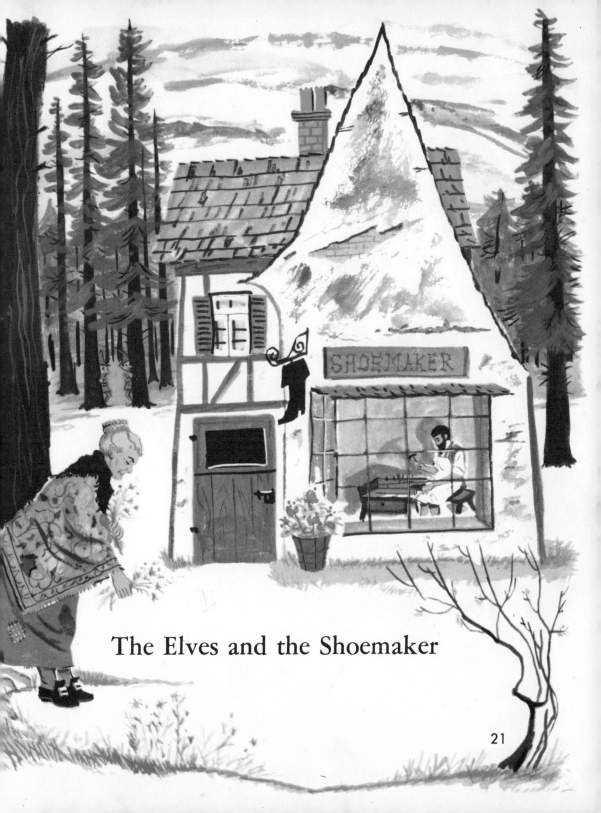

The Elves and the Shoemaker

Once there was a shoemaker.
His name was Mr. Hans. He lived
in a beautiful little house with
Mrs. Hans.

Mr. Hans worked from morning
to night every day to make shoes.
But every day he was poorer and
poorer.

At last he had just one little piece of leather from which to cut shoes.

Hans cut out his last shoes. He was not happy. "Dear me," he thought. "We are so poor now! I do not know how we can buy food in a day or two. Soon we will have no food to eat."

It was night-time when Hans had cut out the shoes. "I will make the shoes tomorrow," he said. Then he went to bed.

In the morning Hans had a big surprise. The shoes he had cut out the night before were made! And they were beautiful.

"Come here, my dear," he called to Mrs. Hans. "My shoes are done as if by magic. Come see them!"

Soon a man came to the
shoemaker's little house. When he
saw the fine new shoes he asked
if he could buy them.

After he had gone Hans could
buy leather for four new shoes. And
Mrs. Hans could go to the store
to get food for them to eat.

That night the shoemaker cut
four shoes from his new piece of
leather. When he got out of bed in
the morning, the four shoes were all
ready for someone to buy. They
were as well made and as pretty as
the shoes had been the day before.

Soon everyone came to buy the
beautiful shoes. And Hans and
Mrs. Hans were very happy.

Day after day Hans would buy more leather and cut out more shoes.

Night after night the fine new shoes would be made.

Men came from far away to look at the shoes and to buy them. Soon Hans and Mrs. Hans had all the food they could eat.

But not once did Hans or Mrs. Hans see who made the shoes.

One night Hans and Mrs. Hans
sat near their fire. It was
a cold night. They could hear the
wind and see the snow through
the window.

28

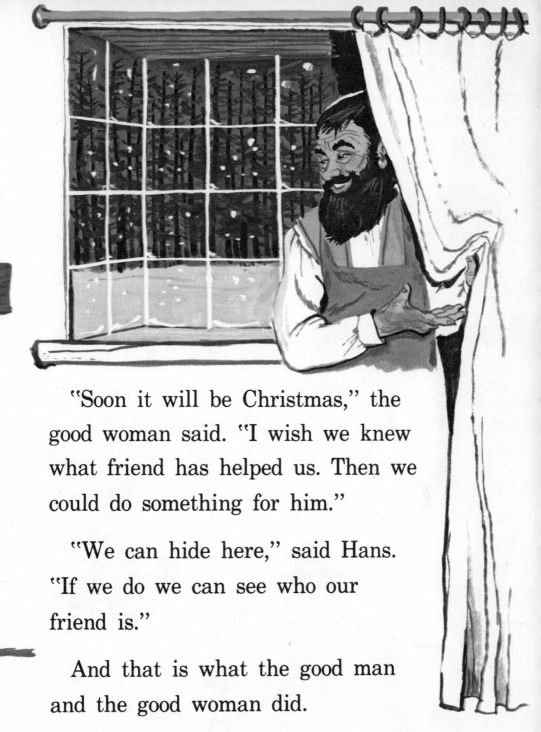

"Soon it will be Christmas," the good woman said. "I wish we knew what friend has helped us. Then we could do something for him."

"We can hide here," said Hans. "If we do we can see who our friend is."

And that is what the good man and the good woman did.

Soon Hans and his wife heard a little noise. They saw the door fly open! In came two little men. They were elves!

The elves were at work in a minute. And how fast they did go! In no time at all the shoes were made and ready for the next day.

When the work was done, the elves opened the door and went away over the cold, white snow.

30

"Oh, the poor little elves!" said
Mrs. Hans. "Did you see their
feet? They have no shoes, and they
had so little on that they were blue
with cold!"

"Hans," the good woman said,
"we must make some shoes and
coats for our friends before
Christmas." And so they did.

It was very near Christmas. Hans and Mrs. Hans worked all day long for five days. Mrs. Hans made two warm red coats. And Hans made warm little green shoes that were just right for the elves' feet.

On the night before Christmas the big surprise was ready for the elves.

Hans put the red coats and leather shoes near the door. After that he and Mrs. Hans just had time to hide.

In the door came two elves. They were cold and had no shoes. Then they saw the beautiful coats and the new shoes. "Look!" said one. "They are for us. They are ours!" And the elves put them on.

What fun they had! They jumped about and sang to show how warm and happy they were. Then they went out and shut the door.

Hans never saw the elves again. But he and his good woman were always happy and had all the food they could eat.

Every Christmas night Mrs. Hans put a little cake near the door. Every Christmas morning the cake was gone. And Mr. and Mrs. Hans could see where the little shoes had come over the snow.

Here's the way we make our shoes, We make our shoes, We make our shoes, Here's the way we make our shoes, So pret – ty In the night.

The Little Shoemakers

Here is the way we make our shoes,
We make our shoes,
We make our shoes,

Here is the way we make our shoes
So pretty
In the night.

36

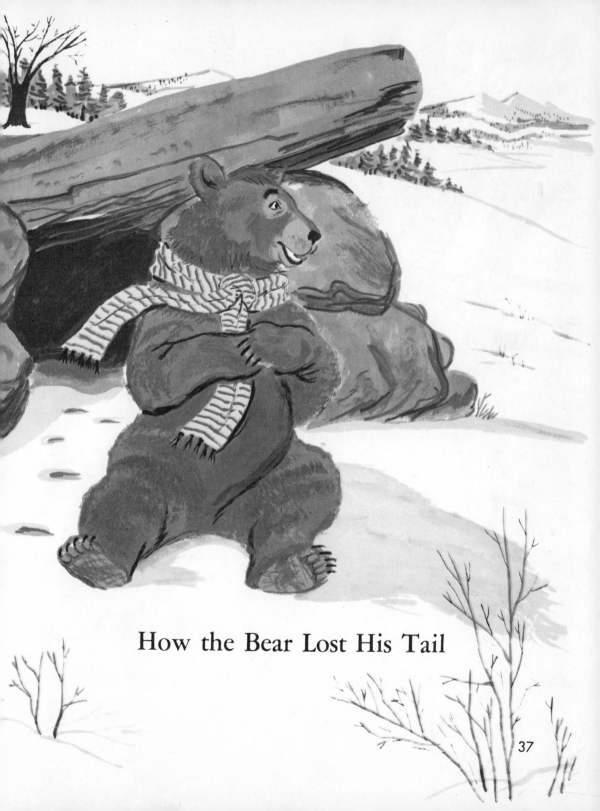

How the Bear Lost His Tail

In the days of old the bear had
a long, beautiful tail. This is the
story of how he lost it.

It was a very cold day. The first
snow was all around. You could not
see the plants in the gardens.

A bear was out in the snow. He
wanted to find something more to
eat before he began his long sleep.

Soon the bear met a bad red fox.
The fox had some fish.

"Good day, Mr. Fox," said the
bear. "Where did you get the fine
fish?"

"I got them from the river," said
Mr. Fox.

"They are beautiful fish!" said
the bear. "Can you show me how
to get some?"

40

"I will be happy to help you, Mr. Bear," the fox said. "After I hide my fish in this old tree we will go to the river. I will show you how to get some fish."

The fox and the bear went over the cold snow to the river. When they got there, the bad fox told the bear what to do to get some fish.

"First," said the fox, "you must
go out on the ice and cut a hole.
Then you must stick your tail
through the hole and into the
water."

The bear did just what the fox
told him to do.

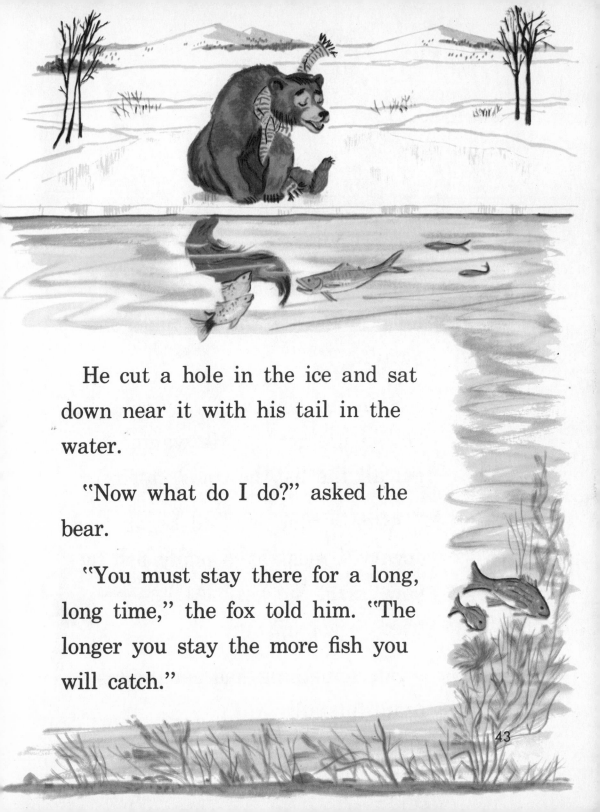

He cut a hole in the ice and sat
down near it with his tail in the
water.

"Now what do I do?" asked the
bear.

"You must stay there for a long,
long time," the fox told him. "The
longer you stay the more fish you
will catch."

The bear sat on the ice for a long time after the fox had gone away.

Soon the bear was very cold. But he did not get up. He wanted to get all the fish he could catch.

After a time the sun began to go down. "I must have many fish by now," said the bear. At last he tried to get up.

But something had caught his beautiful tail!

Poor Mr. Bear could not get his tail out of the hole. His tail was caught in the ice!

He tried and tried to get away, but he could not. At last he tried to jump to get out of the ice. He made a big jump. Off came his tail!

And that is why the bear has gone about with a little tail to this very day.

46

The Three Wishes

There was once a poor farmer
named Paddy. He lived in an old
house with his brother.

The two brothers were not happy.
They wanted a fine house and a
big farm. They wanted many horses
and cows.

47

One day Paddy and his brother
John were at work in their little
garden. They heard someone call
them. "Who can it be?" asked John.

In a minute Paddy said, "I heard
someone cry out again!"

"Yes," said John. "I heard him,
too. I think he is near the trees."

The two brothers ran to see who
had called them. Soon they were
surprised to find a little old man
who was caught under a tree.
Because he was so little John and
Paddy knew him. They knew that
the old man was one of the elves
who lived nearby.

"Well," said the little man.
"Don't just look at me! Help me
get out from under this tree!"

"We will help you," said John.

"Oh, no!" said Paddy. "Let us ask for something first."

"We are very poor, Mr. Elf. Will you give us three wishes if we let you go?" asked Paddy.

The little man did not want to give the brothers three wishes. "Very well," said Paddy. "Then you can stay under that tree all summer!"

At last the elf told the brothers
that they could have the three
wishes. Then Paddy and John
helped him as he crawled out from
under the tree.

"I said you could have three
wishes," the elf told the brothers.
"You can have them. But they will
not make you happy." Then, as if
by magic, he was gone.

Paddy and John went back to
their little old house. They sat
down near the fire. "What should
we wish for?" asked John.

"I think that I am going to wish
for a big farm," said Paddy.

"And I guess that I will wish for
a fine house," said John.

"Then for the last wish we can
ask for many horses and cows,"
Paddy told his brother.

"Let us eat dinner before we make our wishes," said John.

"All right," said Paddy. "But I wish we had a pot of soup ready. Then we could make our wishes now."

Paddy had no sooner made this wish than there was a pot of soup on the hot fire!

"Oh, dear," said John. "Look
what you have done! You have lost
one of our wishes for us."

Then, before John had time to
think of what he was doing, he said,
"I wish that pot of soup were on
your nose!"

And just like that the pot of soup
was on Paddy's nose.

"Now see what you have done,"
said Paddy. "You have made
another wish! Now help me get
this pot off."

But nothing they did helped. The brothers could not get the pot off Paddy's nose.

After a while John said, "Well, we have not used our last wish. I can ask for a big farm, or the fine house, or the horses and cows."

"What!" said Paddy. "And let me go around with this pot of soup on my nose? Never!"

"But, Paddy, if we don't wish for the farm, or the house, or the farm animals, we will never get them. Don't you think you could live with the pot of soup on your nose?"

"Oh, no, I can't do that. We must wish the pot of soup off my nose, John."

At last John said that he would wish the pot off Paddy's nose. He did so and the pot was gone. And so was the last of the wishes.

The elf had been right. John and Paddy had three wishes that they made the little old man give them. But the brothers were not happy. And they were just as poor as they had been before.

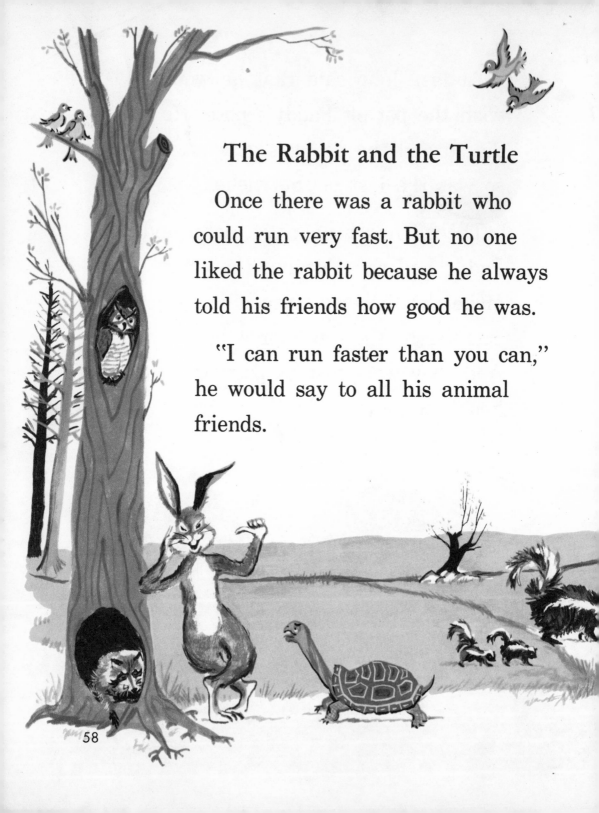

The Rabbit and the Turtle

Once there was a rabbit who could run very fast. But no one liked the rabbit because he always told his friends how good he was.

"I can run faster than you can," he would say to all his animal friends.

At last the turtle had heard all
he wanted to hear about how fast
the rabbit could run.

"You are not so good, Mr. Rabbit,"
said the turtle. "Why, I can run as
fast as you can!"

"You funny old turtle!" said the
rabbit. "I could run from here to
the big tree before you could crawl
to the road."

"Very well, Mr. Rabbit," said the
turtle. "Let us see who can get to
the big tree first."

"I am ready to go now," said the
rabbit and he began to run.

The turtle crawled after him.

It was a warm day. By the time
he came to the road the rabbit
wanted to go to sleep.

The turtle was so far away that
the rabbit could not see him. "I
have time to sleep here in the sun!"
the rabbit said. So he stopped
running, shut his eyes, and went
to sleep.

The old turtle never stopped. He
crawled on and on. He came to the
road and crawled on under the hot
sun.

The turtle wanted to go to sleep, too. It was work for him to go so far, but on he went.

At last the rabbit opened his eyes. He looked across the road. Then, far away, he saw the turtle crawling on his way to the big tree.

The rabbit jumped up in surprise. Then he began to run just as fast as he could go. He ran and ran so that he could get to the big tree before the turtle got there.

But the turtle crawled to the big tree first! The rabbit could not catch up with him.

Never again did the rabbit tell his animal friends how fast he could run. He knew that they would tell him that he could not run as fast as a turtle.

The Fox and the Crow

A crow sat in a tree near a little house. He looked in the open window. He saw some good things to eat.

The crow went to the window. He looked around. There was no one near. He went in and quickly took some food.

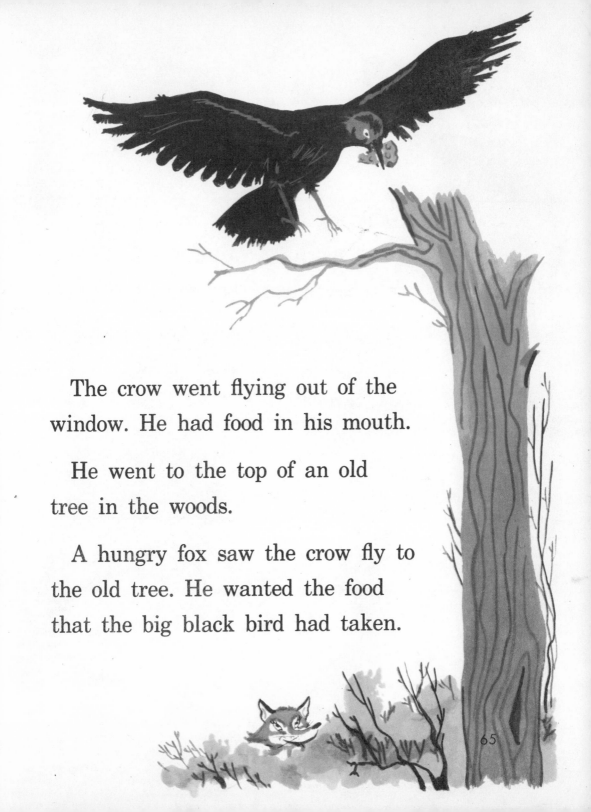

The crow went flying out of the
window. He had food in his mouth.

He went to the top of an old
tree in the woods.

A hungry fox saw the crow fly to
the old tree. He wanted the food
that the big black bird had taken.

The fox went over to the tree.
"Good morning, Mr. Crow," he said.
"You are a very beautiful bird."

This made the crow very happy.
He liked to hear that he was
beautiful.

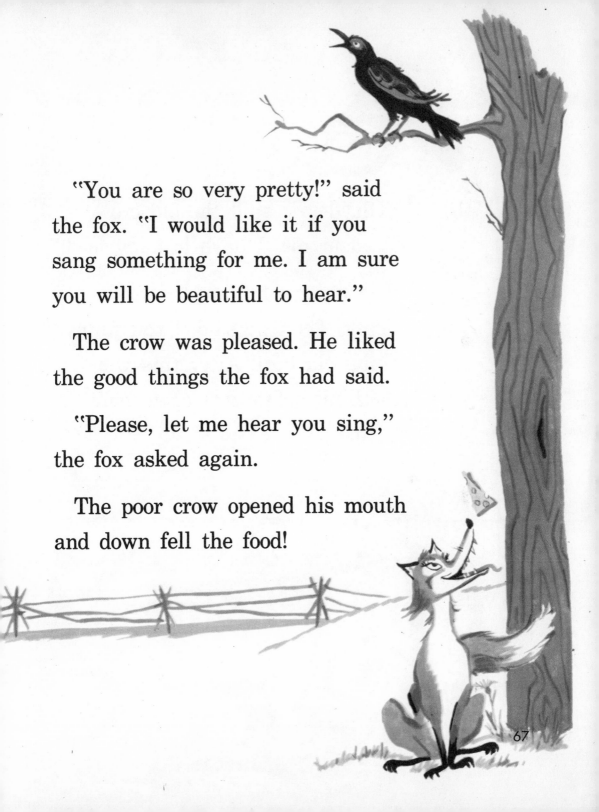

"You are so very pretty!" said
the fox. "I would like it if you
sang something for me. I am sure
you will be beautiful to hear."

The crow was pleased. He liked
the good things the fox had said.

"Please, let me hear you sing,"
the fox asked again.

The poor crow opened his mouth
and down fell the food!

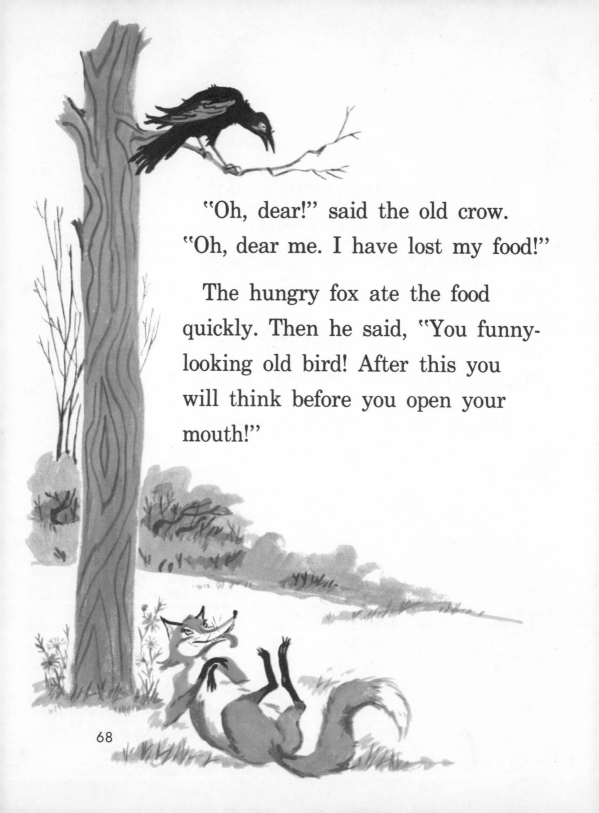

"Oh, dear!" said the old crow. "Oh, dear me. I have lost my food!"

The hungry fox ate the food quickly. Then he said, "You funny-looking old bird! After this you will think before you open your mouth!"

The Boy and the North Wind

A boy once lived with his mother
in a little old house. The house
was on a farm. On the farm there
was a cow.

The farm gave the boy and his
mother a little food to eat. The
cow gave them some milk.

On many cold days the boy and
his mother had very little food.
They were always hungry. For their
dinner they had some gingerbread
and milk.

The North Wind came to their
little home. He made the window
fly open. The milk fell over and ran
under the boy's feet.

"The North Wind can not do this to us," said the boy. "He must give us more milk."

"Yes, Jack," his mother said. "Run after the North Wind. Tell him that he must give us something for the milk."

Jack put on his hat and coat. He ran out of the house. He could see the North Wind. The North Wind was far away across the snow.

"Come back!" Jack called. But the North Wind ran on. Then Jack ran after the bad North Wind.

He ran and ran. He ran through the woods and down an old road. He ran across farms that were white with new snow.

The North Wind went quickly from town to town. He went through the city and across white hills. And Jack came right after him.

73

At last the Wind went to his
home. Jack went up to the door.
The North Wind let him in.

The boy said, "You must give us
something for the milk we lost."

The North Wind wanted to play.
But he was not a bad little man.
"Very well," he said. "Take this
magic gingerbread. You may cut off
as many pieces as you wish. There
will always be more of it to eat!"

Then Jack went on his way. By this time it was morning. He stopped at a farm house. He asked if he could eat and sleep there. The farmer told him to come in.

The farmer was not a good man. He was a bad man. He saw Jack cut pieces from his magic gingerbread. He saw that there was always more gingerbread to eat!

When Jack was sleeping the farmer took the magic gingerbread. He gave Jack some gingerbread that was not magic.

Jack went home with the gingerbread. When he got there he found the gingerbread had lost the magic. When he cut off the last piece there was no more to eat!

The boy went back to the home of
the North Wind. "You must give
me something new," he said. "The
gingerbread is all gone!"

The Wind gave him a magic pot
of soup. Jack could take all the
soup he wanted from the pot. There
was always more in it!

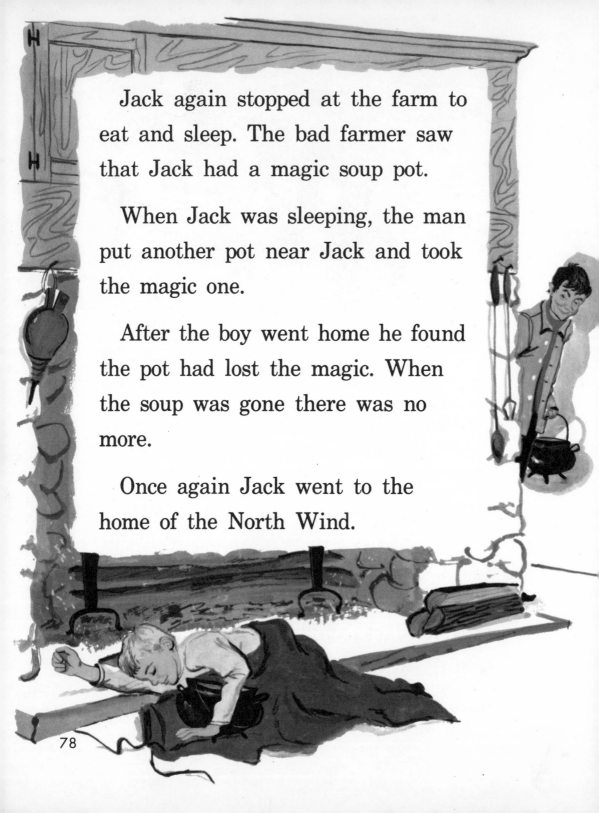

Jack again stopped at the farm to eat and sleep. The bad farmer saw that Jack had a magic soup pot.

When Jack was sleeping, the man put another pot near Jack and took the magic one.

After the boy went home he found the pot had lost the magic. When the soup was gone there was no more.

Once again Jack went to the home of the North Wind.

"This is the last time I will
help you," said the North Wind.

"Take this magic stick," the
Wind told Jack. "It will help you
if you say 'Work, stick, work!' "

"Thank you. Thank you very
much," said Jack. Then he began
to make his way home.

Once more Jack stopped at the farm house. The farmer was pleased to see him. He asked Jack to come in to eat and sleep.

The bad farmer saw Jack's stick. He was sure that it was a magic stick. When Jack was sleeping, the farmer took the stick.

Just then Jack opened his eyes. "Work, stick, work!" he called out. And the stick began to go after the farmer.

Again and again it came down on the bad man. "Help! Help!" cried the farmer. "Stop your stick and I will give back your magic gingerbread. I will give back the magic pot."

"Stop, stick, stop!" said Jack, and the stick jumped back to the boy.

"Now give me my magic gingerbread. Give me my magic pot," said Jack. "Or I will tell the stick to go after you again!"

The farmer quickly gave up the gingerbread. He gave up the magic pot.

Jack went home. And every day after that Jack and his mother had all they wanted to eat!

What are lit - tle boys made of?

What are lit - tle boys made of?

 and ⟨snail⟩ and lit - tle dogs' tails, That's

what lit - tle boys are made of.

What Are Little Boys Made Of?

What are little boys made of?
What are little boys made of?

and and little
dogs' tails,
That's what little boys are made of.

84

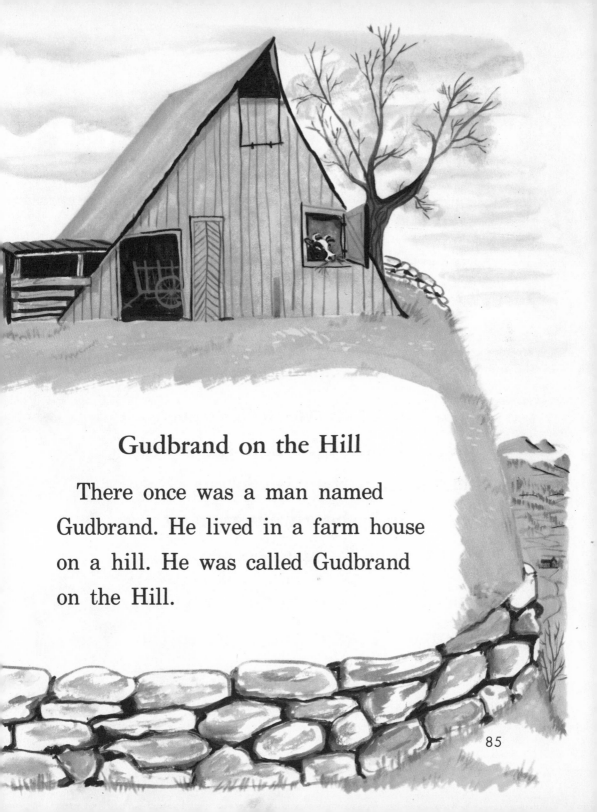

Gudbrand on the Hill

There once was a man named
Gudbrand. He lived in a farm house
on a hill. He was called Gudbrand
on the Hill.

Mrs. Gudbrand was a very good
woman. She thought that there was
no better man than Gudbrand.
What he did, she always thought
was the right thing to do.

One day the good woman said to
Gudbrand, "I want you to go to the
city. Get some money for our cow
so that we can buy food to eat."

Gudbrand went down the hill with the cow. The city was far away.

On the way to the city Gudbrand met a man. The man had a very old horse. He said to Gudbrand, "I will give you my fine horse for your little old cow."

"All right," said Gudbrand, and he gave away his fine cow.

After a while Gudbrand met a little old woman. She had a big brown dog.

"Good day," said the woman.

"Good day," said Gudbrand.

"What a poor old horse you have," she said. "Take my fine dog and I will give your horse a good home and good food to eat."

Gudbrand took the dog and went on his way to the town. Before he got there he met a boy. The boy gave Gudbrand a white kitten for the brown dog.

At last Gudbrand came to the
little city. He had come a long
way. He was hungry. The kitten
was hungry, too.

Then Gudbrand saw a man who
had some cakes and milk. "Please
let me buy some cake," said
Gudbrand. "Let me buy some milk
for my little white cat."

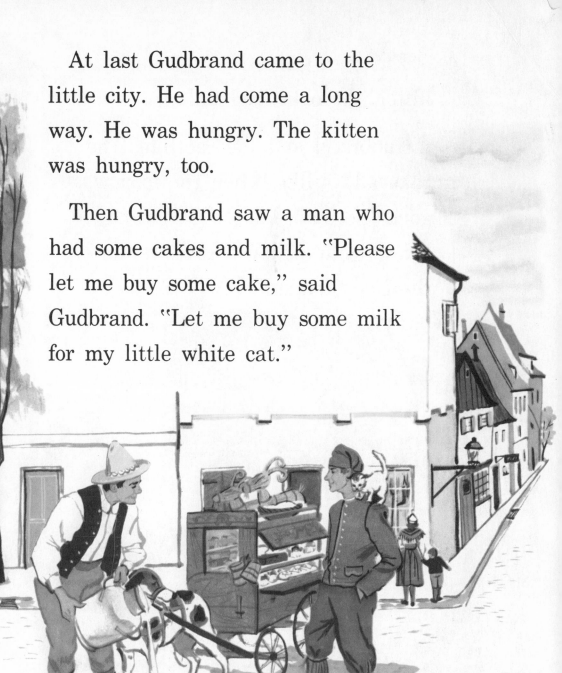

The man gave Gudbrand and his kitten the cake and milk.

Gudbrand and the cat liked the cake and milk. When the food was gone the man said to Gudbrand, "Now what will you give me for the cake and milk?"

"I have nothing but my kitten to give," said Gudbrand. "But he is a fine kitten! I gave my cow for a horse. I gave my horse for a dog. Then I gave the dog for this kitten. So you can see that he must be a very fine kitten."

The man took Gudbrand's kitten for the cake and milk.

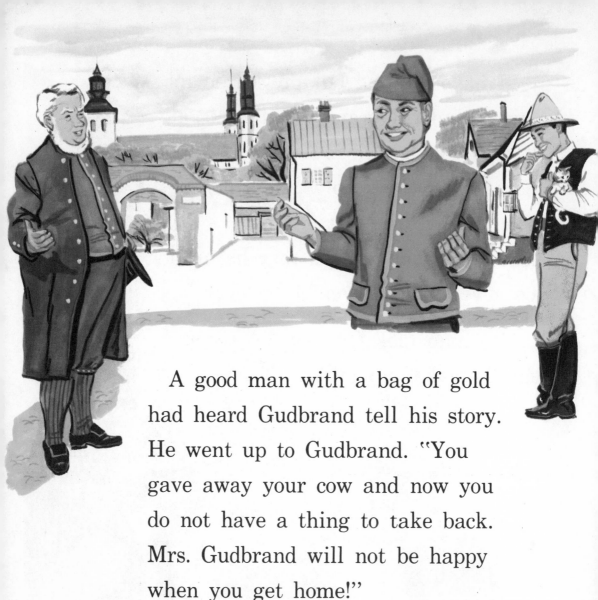

A good man with a bag of gold
had heard Gudbrand tell his story.
He went up to Gudbrand. "You
gave away your cow and now you
do not have a thing to take back.
Mrs. Gudbrand will not be happy
when you get home!"

"Oh, yes she will," said Gudbrand.
"I have a good woman. She will be
happy when I tell her what I did."

"If Mrs. Gudbrand is happy when you tell her what you got for the cow, I will give you five pieces of gold," the man with the gold said.

"And if she is not happy," said Gudbrand, "I will give you my farm."

Gudbrand took the good man to his home on the side of the hill. When they got there the man said, "I will hide here by the door. Then I can hear what your wife has to say!"

Gudbrand went into the house.
Mrs. Gudbrand came to see him.
"Did you get the money for our
cow?" she asked. "What did you
get for her?"

Gudbrand told his story so that
the good man with the bag of gold
could hear him. "Well, my dear,"
he said, "I gave the cow to a man
for his horse."

"That is good," said Mrs.
Gudbrand. "Now we will have a
horse to ride."

"But then I gave the horse to a
little old woman who gave me a
dog."

"That is better," said Mrs.
Gudbrand. "I have wanted a dog
for a long time."

"But then I gave the dog to a
little boy. He gave me a white
kitten for the dog."

95

"So much the better," the good woman said. "I like cats, and we do not have one."

"But when I got to town I was hungry," said Gudbrand. "I gave the kitten to a man for some cake and milk."

"You did just the right thing," said Mrs. Gudbrand. "I would not want you to go hungry. Now come and sit down to dinner."

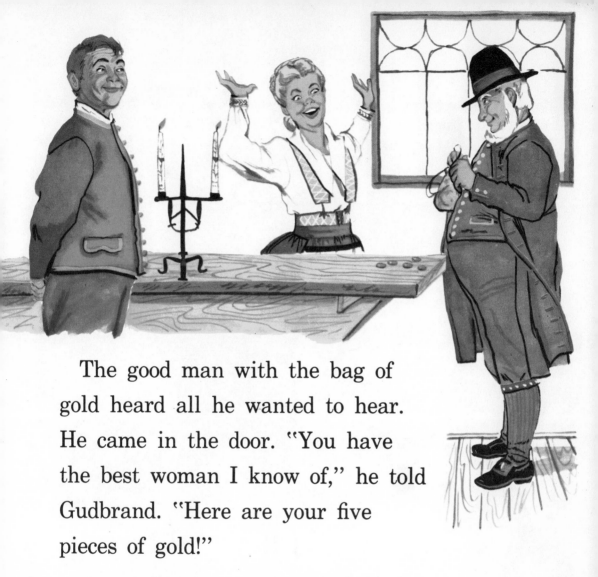

The good man with the bag of
gold heard all he wanted to hear.
He came in the door. "You have
the best woman I know of," he told
Gudbrand. "Here are your five
pieces of gold!"

And that is how Gudbrand on the
Hill gave away his cow for milk
and cake but got five pieces of
gold.

The Cat and the Milk

There was once an old woman who had a black cat.

One day the old woman milked her cow.

"Now I must go to town," she said. "Where can I put this milk so the cat will not get it?

"I know! I will put it in this jug! It is so little that my cat can not crawl into it!"

After the old woman had gone to town the cat said, "Now how can I get that milk?"

The cat tried and tried. But he could not crawl into the jug to get some milk.

After a while he sat down to think. At last he said, "I have it! I know how I can get that milk!"

The cat ran out of the house. He came back with some stones. He put the stones into the jug. Each time he put in a stone the milk came nearer the top of the jug.

After a while the milk came right to the top of the jug. The cat could have all the milk he wanted!

When the little old woman came
home she saw what the cat had
done.

"Well!" said she, "this is the
last time I let you into the house.
After this you will go to town
with me!"

My

I have a little that goes
    in and out with me,
And what can be the use of him is
    more than I can see.
He is very, very like me from

    up to the head;
And I see him jump before me, when
    I jump into my bed.

The Bear, the Man, and the Fox

One day a big black bear was caught in a trap. He tried and tried to get out.

At last he cried for help. "Please, please!" he called. "Will someone get me out of here?"

A man heard the bear calling. He ran to see why the bear was crying for help.

When the bear saw the man he said, "Dear friend, let me out."

"Oh, no!" said the man. "If I let you out you will eat me."

"It is not so!" said the black
bear. "I will be your friend. I will
give you anything you want. Just
please let me out."

At last the good man gave in. He
opened the door to the trap.

Out jumped the bear. He caught
the man. "Now I will eat you up!"
he said. "I was in the trap a long
time. I am very hungry."

"Stop!" said the man. "Let us
ask the first three things we see
if it is all right for you to eat me."

"Very well," said the bear. "You
may ask the first three things that
we see. I am sure they will say
that I may eat you up."

The first thing they met was a
tree. "Why, sure, the bear may eat
you," the tree said. "I am good to
men and what do they do to me
and my brothers? They cut us up
and put us in their fires!

"Be a man! Let the bear eat you!"

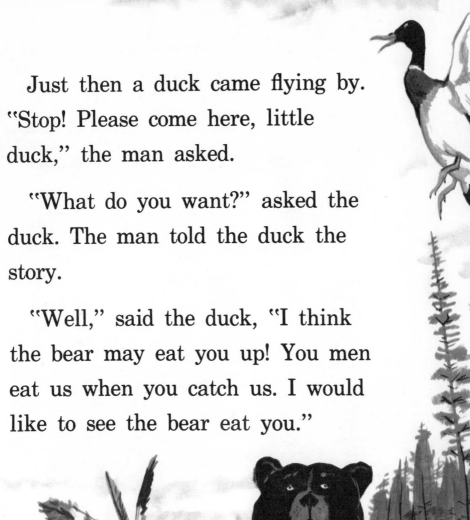

Just then a duck came flying by.
"Stop! Please come here, little
duck," the man asked.

"What do you want?" asked the
duck. The man told the duck the
story.

"Well," said the duck, "I think
the bear may eat you up! You men
eat us when you catch us. I would
like to see the bear eat you."

After the duck had gone away the bear and the man met a fox.

"Dear friend fox," said the man, "we want you to hear our story."

He began to tell how he had let the big animal out of the trap. He made the story just as long as he could.

"Oh dear," said the fox. "Now how did you say this all began? You say you were in the trap and the bear let you out?"

"No! No!" said the bear. "I was in the trap."

"Oh, yes. I see! I was in the trap," said the fox. "No, I was not in the trap. Dear me! Who was in the trap?"

The bear began over again. "I said I was in the trap. The man let me out."

"But how could the man let me out?" asked the fox. "I was not in the trap."

"Now look here," said the bear.
"I will show you how it was. I am
the bear. This is the trap. I will
now go back into the trap."

The big animal went back into
the trap. "This is where the man
found me," said the bear.

The fox quickly shut the door of
the trap.

"Oh," said the fox. "Now I see how it was! You were in the trap, Mr. Bear. The man came by the door. He let you out. Now you are back in the trap!"

"Yes! Yes!" said the bear. "Now let me out again."

"Oh, no!" said the fox. "If I may say so, I think you are just where you had better be!"

Snow-White and Rose-Red

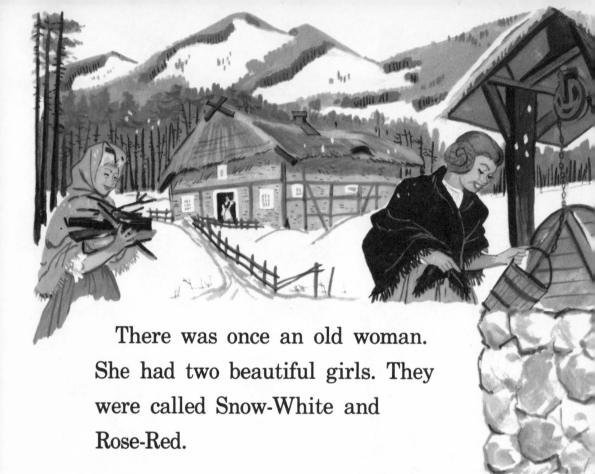

There was once an old woman.
She had two beautiful girls. They
were called Snow-White and
Rose-Red.

The two girls were as good as
they could be. They always liked to
help their mother. They made the
beds and helped to get dinner
ready. Snow-White would make the
fire each night. Rose-Red would
bring water from the well.

One cold night the girls sat by the fire. All at once they heard someone at the door. "See who it is," said Mother to Snow-White.

Snow-White ran to the door. "Who is there?" she asked.

117

"Please let me in. I am cold,"
someone said.

"Open the door," said Mother.
"It is some poor man who has been
out in the snow."

Snow-White opened the door. A
big black bear put his head into
the room. The girl cried out and
jumped back!

"Do not be afraid," said the bear.
"I just want to get warm by your
fire."

"Do come in," said Mother to the
bear. "But do not go too near the
fire. Your fine coat might catch
on fire."

119

The bear came to the little house
every night after that. Snow-White
and Rose-Red had fun playing with
him.

Every night the bear would sleep
near the fire. In the morning he
would go away.

At last the snows were over.
"Now," said the bear, "I must go
away. I will not be back until it
snows again."

"Why must you go, dear bear?"
asked Snow-White and Rose-Red.

"I hide my gold in the far-away hills," said the bear. "I must keep my eye on it. If I do not, a bad old elf will take it from me. He sleeps all the time it is cold. Now that it is warm he will get up and look for my gold!"

The bear said good-by to the girls. They were not happy to see him go. But they were happy to hear that he would come back when the snow fell again.

Some time after that the mother asked the girls to go to town. She told them to buy new coats and shoes. "And buy some milk, too," she said.

The road to town went across a river. It went through a woods where there were big trees. It took the girls by pretty farms where flowers were growing in the little gardens.

On their way home the girls
heard someone calling for help.
They ran around the big trees.

Soon they came to an opening
in the woods. There they found a
little old man. It was the elf who
lived in the woods.

125

A big bird had caught the elf.
It tried to fly away with him. Rose-
Red found a big stick. She went
after the big bird. She tried to
make the bird let go of the little
man.

At last the big bird gave up. He
let the elf go. The girls and the
little man saw him fly away over
the tree tops.

The elf took off his hat. He thanked the girls for helping him. Then he said, "What can I do for you? I can work magic. Would you like me to give you a new house? Or a puppy? Or a fine, fat cow to give you milk? I will give you what you ask for."

The girls looked at one another. Then Rose-Red asked, "Do you know a big black bear who lives in the woods near here?"

127

After a minute the little old man said, "Yes, I know the bear."

"Well," said Snow-White, "we want you to stop taking his gold! Then he will not have to look after it all summer long. He can come back to our house to play."

For a long time the little man
did not say a thing. Then he said,
"Very well. Come with me to the
bear's house."

He took the girls through the
woods. He took them up the side of
a hill on which the bear lived. At
last they came to a hole in the
hill.

"Come out, Mr. Bear, come out,"
the little old man called.

When the bear came out the old
man said, "I am going to tell the
girls a story.

"Three years ago a fine-looking
man was going through the woods.
He had a bag of gold. When he
would not give me the gold I did
something very bad. I used my
magic to make him into a bear.

"Because you girls helped me I
will never again take the gold.
What is more, I will make this bear
back into a man," the old elf said.

And he did just that!

When the bear had been made
back into a man the first thing he
said was, "Thank you, Rose-Red!
Thank you, Snow-White!

"Because you are good as well as
beautiful you have helped this
little old man. You have helped me.

"Now I am going to give each of
you some of my gold. I know you
will use it well."

Snow-White and Rose-Red said
good-by and ran home. They lived
for many years. They were always
happy and they were always good
to others.

Rain Fairies

Rain fairies playing on my garden
bed,
Each little flower puts up its head.

Sun fairies laugh and see the
flowers play.
Now, little rain fairies, you must
fly away.

Fly to your cloud home, far up in

the
Come, little sun fairies; rain
fairies, good-by.

The Wind and the Sun

One fine day the Wind met the Sun.

"I am better than you are," said the Wind to the Sun.

"Oh, no," said the Sun. "I am the better of the two."

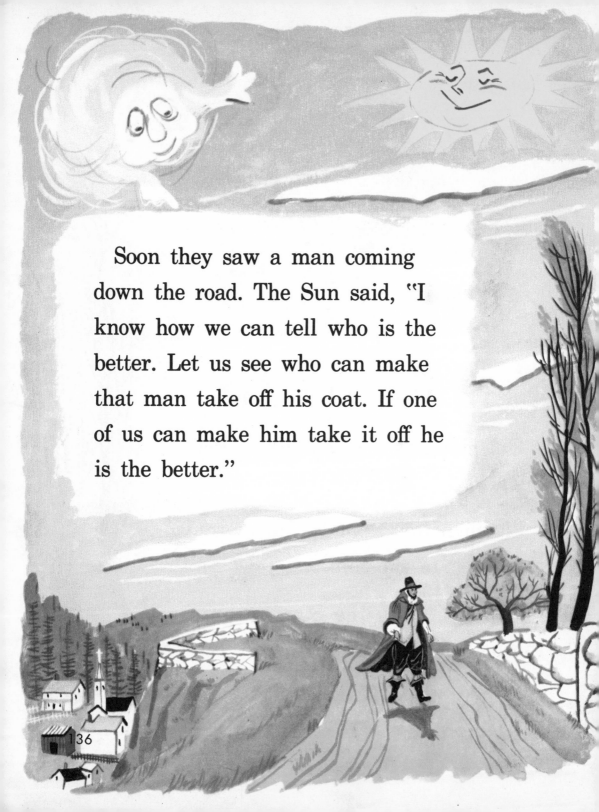

Soon they saw a man coming down the road. The Sun said, "I know how we can tell who is the better. Let us see who can make that man take off his coat. If one of us can make him take it off he is the better."

"All right, Mr. Sun," said the Wind. "You go in back of a cloud. I will show you how quickly I can get the man out of his coat!"

The Wind made a big noise. He tried to get the man out of his coat. He tried and tried! But all the man did was to draw his coat more closely around him.

At last the Wind gave up. "Come out of the cloud, Mr. Sun," he said. "I for one can not get this man to take off his coat."

The Sun now began to come through the clouds. He made everything very warm. Soon the man on the road opened his coat.

Then the Sun began to get hot. In two minutes the man took off his coat.

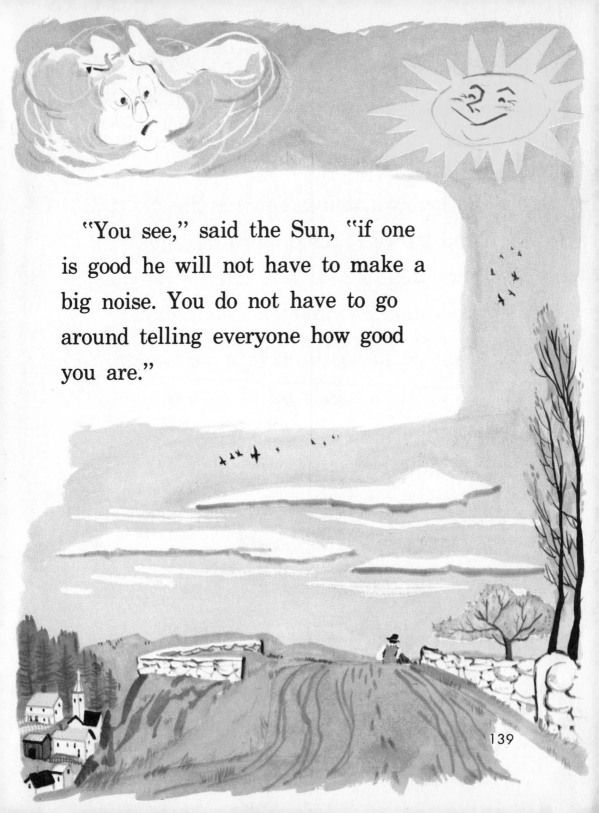

"You see," said the Sun, "if one is good he will not have to make a big noise. You do not have to go around telling everyone how good you are."

For Every Day

Father, we thank You for the night,
And for the pretty morning light;
For tales to read and friends for play,
And all that makes a happy day.

Help us to do the things we should,
To be to others kind and good;
In all we do in work or play,
To grow better in every way.

Word List

One of the unique features of *Storyland Favorites* is the close correlation of the vocabulary with the vocabularies of leading basal reading series. If *Storyland Favorites* is used after the completion of the Second Reader of your basal reading series, pupils will encounter only a very few new words in *Storyland Favorites*.

A list of words new to the basic-reader vocabulary which you use in your classroom, together with page numbers on which these words first appear in *Storyland Favorites*, is found in the Teachers' Manual for *Storyland Favorites*.

The following words from *Storyland Favorites* are listed in special groups, as an aid to the teacher in helping children learn any of the words which are new to them.

Proper nouns:

Gudbrand	Hans	Jack	John	Paddy

Words which can be learned from picture clues:

brother	elves	leather	river	summer
cloud	eyes	lion	shoemaker	tail
coats	gold	men	soup	trap
crow	hole	mouth	stick	wife
elf	jug	pot	stones	woods

Words which can be learned from phonic and structural clues (the known word is given in parentheses following the new word):

anything (any, thing)	rose (nose)	tops (hops)
knew (grew)	show (know)	tried (cried)
near (hear)	shut (but)	years (hears)
right (night)	sing (bring)	

Words which can be learned from context:

beautiful	minute	poor	their
been	north	quickly	through
each	piece	sure	while

141